The Adventures of Buffalo Bill and Cody

"Crossing the Pecos"

An Exciting Story of Real Live Buffalo

By: Elisabeth Prude Longbotham
and
Dr. Jack H. Longbotham

The Young West Collection
Book Two

Dedicated with love and prayers to our very special grandchildren
and to all young people everywhere who love the West.
Psalm 78 vs. 4-8
Hebrews 6 vs. 12

Illustrations by: Dr. Jack Longbotham
Color by: Kevin Hagan
Printing: Conley Printing Company
Bindery: H.V. Chapman and Sons

The Adventures of Buffalo Bill and Cody
Crossing the Pecos
ISBN 0-9645947-1-4
Copyright © 1996
By Elisabeth Prude Longbotham
and Dr. Jack Longbotham
P.O. Drawer LL
Clyde, Texas 79510

Published by
Western Heritage Publishing
P.O. Box 3703
Abilene, Texas 79604

Morning time comes to the Real West and Buffalo Bill and Cody wake up to a bright new morning. The big, round, red sun rises slowly over the high mountains. This is the beginning of a beautiful day.

Psalm 143 vs. 8

one

Cody is the first to start moving. She begins to get up – back legs first – then front legs. She stands tall and stre - e - e - tches ever so slowly. It feels so good to be wide awake.

Buffalo Bill is so warm and comfortable on his bed of grass. He is still resting — but not for long! Cody is making so much noise moving around in the tall grass and over the rocks! <u>Now</u> Bill is awake!

Bill gets up on his feet trying to really wake up. He blinks his sleepy eyes and begins to lead Cody from their resting place. The buffalo begin grazing along the mountain trail. The best green grass is down the Southwest Canyon, so on their way they go.

four

High noon comes, the hot sun is overhead and Bill and Cody are very thirsty. A stop at the bend of Limpia Creek will give them a cool drink of mountain water and that will be so good!

Psalm 136 vs. 8

five

The two big, brown, thirsty buffalo walk to the edge of the clear water. As a mirror reflects an image — so the still, smooth water does the same. Bill and Cody look into the water and see their own reflections — fuzzy heads, big horns, brown eyes and wide black noses.

Psalm 23 vs. 2

Look! There is something mysterious! What is this? One buffalo —
two buffalo — SURPRISE — three buffalo in the reflections in the water! Is it
real? Can Bill and Cody believe what they are seeing?

Yes! Standing nearby is another buffalo! Bill and Cody jerk their heads up, step back from the creek and quickly make a shocking discovery. There, right before their eyes, is a pretty girl buffalo.

She was shy and very frightened. Her head was down, but she tried hard to switch her tail in a friendly way. Her name was Rattlehorn, an Indian name, and she was so glad to see Bill and Cody.

Rattlehorn had been chased away by the big herd of buffalo over the mountains. The buffalo were very unkind and did not want her roaming with them because she was different. They always pushed her and ran at her with their big sharp horns and strong shoulders. Rattlehorn was always the last buffalo in the herd to eat and drink.

Rattlehorn was just roaming by the creek looking for some peace and quiet. She had about decided just to live alone after being chased day after day, most of her life. She was very lonely and sad. Rattlehorn was not sure if she would ever be a happy buffalo again.

Rattlehorn was a little different, but she could not change that now. When she was young, she had an accident and her left horn was hurt. As she grew up, the horn did not grow straight like her other horn. It was a low, droopy horn and not real tight against her head. When she ran, the horn made a rattling sound and because of these differences, she had no friends in the big buffalo herd.

twelve

Rattlehorn did not understand why different was so bad, but she wanted very much to have friends. Maybe – just maybe – different could be good! When she saw Bill and Cody she knew she had one more chance to have friends. She was almost afraid to walk near the creek close to the buffalo. In her quiet, shy way she would show courage. Yes! Rattlehorn would try to make friends one more time. If Bill and Cody were unkind to her like the big herd of buffalo, then she would live alone forever in the Davis Mountains.

Buffalo Bill and Cody liked the surprise of having a new buffalo friend. They slowly looked Rattlehorn over and sniffed of her brown coat of hair. Over and over they made a warm welcome noise. Bill and Cody snorted in such a way that Rattlehorn knew she was loved. This was Bill and Cody's way of telling Rattlehorn she was wanted – really wanted – for sure.

fourteen

Cody and Bill wanted Rattlehorn to really feel welcome, so they began to circle around her. Around and around the buffalo went. Soon Rattlehorn held her head up and began to circle around with them. All three buffalo were running in circles first slowly, then faster and faster. This is the way buffalo behave when they meet a new friend.

The three buffalo ran and ran as they were enjoying being together. They chased playfully after making many circles, running and puffing all the while. As they ran, Bill, Cody and Rattlehorn began bouncing and springing into the air on all four legs. This was fun and they were so happy!

Rattlehorn was excited! She was different, but she was loved! No longer would she be alone in the mountains. She could go with Bill and Cody as they went off down the trail. The buffalo stayed close together as they turned to go down the rocky mountain side below Wild Rose Pass. This is a high pass where beautiful roses bloom near by. As they leave the pass, they will discover new range land while traveling toward the Pecos River.

Ecclesiastes 3 vs. 11

A new day dawns, and Rattlehorn is up early and ready to go. Her excitement over the adventures with true friends makes her so happy. She had Bill and Cody on their feet and ready to go at break of day. Today they would look ahead to wide open land, leaving beautiful Star Mountain behind.

Psalm 25 vs. 21

Bill was the leader, always making a way that was safe for Cody and Rattlehorn to follow. The next few days would be the hardest, with little rest as they traveled through the dry flat land. They moved on faster and faster from one water hole to another, as they journeyed toward the new grass land and the Pecos River.

The buffalo found a good place to rest for the night. Bluestem grass was standing tall and the Pecos River could not be too far away. Rattlehorn could not sleep. She was still so excited over her new found friends she just wanted to be near them. She wanted to be close, so she got up and stood watch over Bill and Cody as they slept.

Proverbs 3 vs. 24

Rattlehorn heard a strange noise, and it was close by! First she heard a low growling sound, then it was louder and closer. Trouble was near her sleeping friends! There, very close to Bill and Cody were snarling, growling wolves.

The old enemy, the gray wolf had returned! This time there were two more wolves and all three were sneaking up on the buffalo. The wolves had been following Bill, Cody and Rattlehorn on the trail, waiting for a good chance to attack.

Deuteronomy 31 vs. 6

Rattlehorn turned quickly toward the wolves. With her head down, running fast, horn rattling she charged with all her strength, meeting the wolves head on. Rattlehorn bumped the first wolf with her good horn and the strange rattling noise of the droopy horn frightened all the wolves away. The wolves ran off yelping in the night, never to return! Rattlehorn's great courage had saved her special friends, Bill and Cody.

The rain began to fall as the weary buffalo traveled northeast and suddenly came upon the Pecos River. The river was running swiftly with water from the rains, but they must cross over. The three buffalo moved slowly into the river with brave Bill leading the way. There were deep holes and the water was rushing fast down stream. It was so scary! Bill knew this was not safe, so he found a way out of the water away from danger. Now, he must find a new and better place to cross the river.

Jeremiah 33 vs. 3

The buffalo moved slowly along the edge of the Pecos River, searching for a crossing place. The river would get deeper and run faster very soon, so they must hurry. Soon Bill found a safe way to cross the big river. This place was Horsehead Crossing, and it was a good way to go through the deep water. Many buffalo herds has used this crossing before, so they would too.

Finally, Bill, Cody and Rattlehorn had crossed the Pecos!

Psalm 18 vs. 30

The buffalo came up out of the water and walked up the steep east side. It felt so good to shake the water out of their shaggy hair and know they were safely across the river. The buffalo had proven that by helping each other they could overcome hard times while roaming through the Real West. This was a happy day because they had crossed the Pecos River!

At last, Bill, Cody and Rattlehorn could rest and look far ahead to new horizons.